NAKED
SEX
POSITIONS

NAKED SEX POSITIONS
by Anders Jorgens

Medco Books, LOS ANGELES 90035

1. This is the classic position, adopted by most of the Western World. The man lies on top of the woman, whose legs are spread to give ease of access to the vagina. Both partners are able to kiss, but since the man must support his weight on his arms, he is not able to caress the woman. He is in sole control of the degree and force of penetration, however, while the woman is quite able to caress his body.

2. This variation of the previous position shows the woman's legs closed, and the man's spread on either side of her. This can only be achieved after penetration, and although it frequently results in increased pressure on the penis, it does limit the man's movements to some extent.

3. Here the woman's legs are again spread. The man's weight is now supported on his toes, and hands. The inclined position of the man's torso enables greater freedom of movement, but although this results in a better degree of stimulation, it is not possible for the man to penetrate very deeply.

4. The man lies on his side, between the woman's spread legs, his thigh resting on her raised leg. The woman thus helps to support the man. This results in a very even distribution of weight which makes this a particularly untaxing position. Penetration is good, and the man has considerable freedom of movement.

5. By wrapping her leg around the man's thigh, the woman makes it possible not only for the man to achieve deeper penetration, but she is also free to take a more active part in the proceedings if she wishes.

6. A return to the classic position, except that the woman's legs are bent back under her from the knee. Thus the vagina is completely exposed, and the man is completely in control of the degree and force of penetration. This position does, however, place a strain on the thighs and hips of the woman, and most women will be unable to maintain it for long periods.

7. Another variation of the classic position which is commonly adopted. Access to the vagina is increased by the woman bending her legs, and many women find that this action makes for greater comfort. Her role is, however, essentially passive, although the man has great freedom of movement in penetration.

8. The woman draws her parted knees down towards her breasts, and rests her heels on the man's buttocks. The position allows maximum penetration, and is considered to be particularly favourable for conception. The man is able to move freely.

9. The woman now raises her legs even higher, and links her ankles at the small of the man's back. In this position, penetration is so deep that the man can usually feel the top of the cervix which can greatly stimulate the woman. This depth of penetration also enables the man's body to rub against the clitoris.

10. The man bends one leg, supporting his weight on the knee. One of the woman's legs is hooked over his shoulder. Penetration thus takes place at a slight angle, increasing the man's stimulation. He also has one hand free with which to caress the woman.

11. The woman's legs are now bent back, with the thighs held closely together, the lower legs protruding over the man's shoulders. Not only is penetration exceptionally good, but the closeness of the woman's thighs produces pressure on the penis within the vagina. The man is still able to move freely.

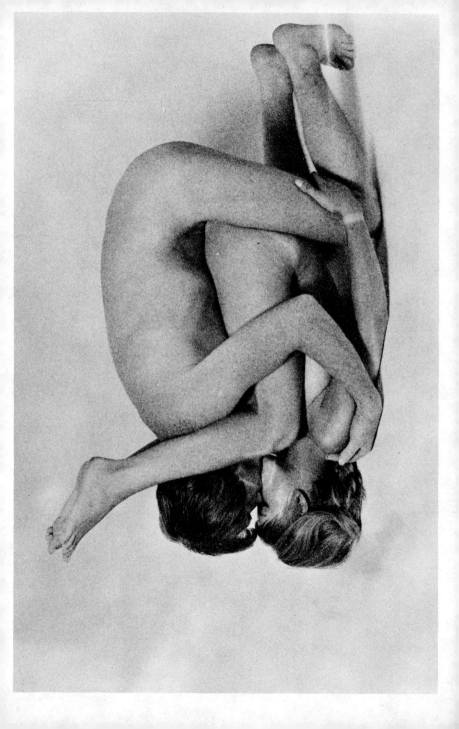

12. The woman has now lifted even more of her body, and extends her legs over her own head, supporting her hips with her hands. This position allows extra deep thrusts by the man, and is equally exciting for both. However, the woman is liable to experience muscular strain quite quickly, and the position should not be maintained for long.

13. The kneeling man draws the woman's body upwards and forwards on to his penis. The woman can take some of her weight on her feet. The position is best for short, rapid, jabbing movements by the man, while the woman is able to wriggle her hips and so increase stimulation both for herself, and her partner.

14. The kneeling man now supports the woman's entire weight. She is impaled upon his penis but both are able to make limited movements. Again this is a tiring position, and should not be maintained for long.

15. The man and the women assume identical positions, the woman's body being over the man's. The weight is taken easily by the hands. The woman must take the initiative here, but her movements are limited.

16. The couple lie side by side, facing each other, and are free to embrace and kiss. Most couples will find the position easier to assume, if penetration takes place with the man on top. The woman then closes her legs, and the couple roll on to their sides. Penetration is not deep, however, and movements have to be carefully controlled if the penis is not to slip out. Many people prefer to use this position without penetration, for the erect penis can then be rubbed against the clitoris producing pleasurable sensations for both partners.

17. Here the woman has drawn her legs up, and the man lies diagonally between them. Penetration is reasonably good, but the movements are necessarily limited.

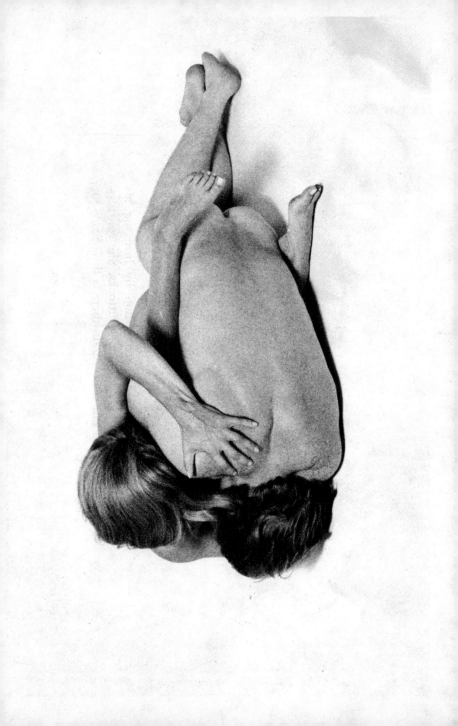

18. The man increases penetration by bringing his knees up towards the woman's buttocks. She can support herself on one arm. Again there is little scope for movement.

19. By opening her legs wider, and placing them around the man, the woman enables greater penetration. The man is also afforded greater freedom of movement, but the position is liable to be tiring for the woman.

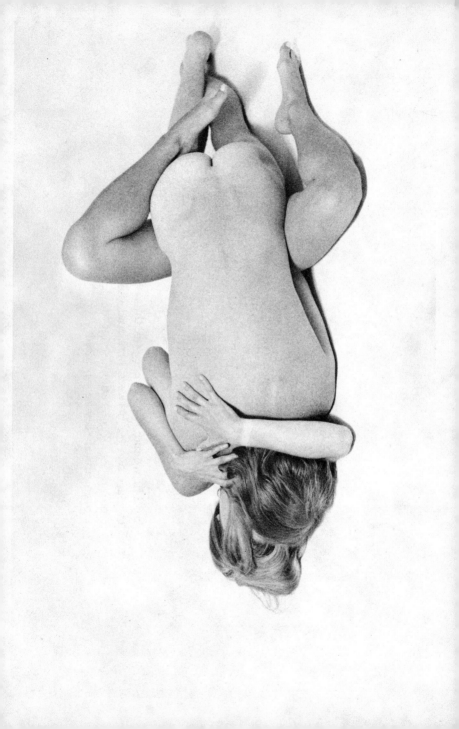

20. The woman curls one leg up, thus enabling the man to place one leg between hers, and the other over her crooked leg. Penetration is not deep, however, and movements are severely limited.

21. The woman lies face downwards, with the man on top of her. Penetration is effected from behind, but is not deep, and any but the most controlled movements can cause the penis to slip out. However, by flexing the muscles of her buttocks, the woman can exert considerable pressure on the penis.

22: This is the most common of the rear entry positions. Penetration is good, and the man has a great deal of freedom to move. His hands are free to caress the woman, who is unable to make much movement.

23. A variation of the previous position which affords, in many cases, even deeper penetration. Movements are good, and often stimulate the clitoris. The man is still able to caress his partner, who remains passive.

24. A further variation, in which the woman is lifted upwards by the man, who supports her weight at the thighs. Her legs extend beyond him, and considerable strain is placed on her arms. Penetration is extremely good, but movements are limited.

25. This is a very difficult position. The woman curls over, her knees placed beyond her shoulders. Facing her, the man is best able to penetrate her by straddling her body in a squatting position. Penetration is often good, but deep movements, though possible, are liable to cause the penis to slip out. The position is, of course, very tiring, and quickly becomes painful for any but the most athletic of women.

26. The penis is introduced from behind, with the couple lying side by side. Entry and penetration are best effected if the woman keeps her back straight, and moves her hips back towards the man. Even so, penetration is not deep, and movement is limited.

27. By bending one leg, the woman makes the entry easier, and enables deeper penetration. This position is often very stimulating, particularly for the woman who, however, may find that she tires quickly.

28. Here, the man places his leg over the woman's. If he now lies at an angle to her, penetration is good and stimulating, but great freedom of movement is not possible.

29. If the woman turns slightly on to her front, and the man firmly embraces her thigh with his leg, the movements he is then able to make often produce greater stimulation of the woman.

30. After penetration, the woman hooks her leg back behind the man. This enables the man to stimulate the clitoris, although penetration is necessarily shallow.

31. The man lies on his back, while the woman straddles him. By supporting her weight on her hands, the woman enables her partner to caress her breasts. Penetration is good, and even the slightest movements, which are recommended because the penis is liable to slip out easily, provide the woman with excellent stimulation. She is, of course, responsible for making the movements.

32. In this variation of the previous position, movement is seriously curtailed, but penetration is good, and the woman experiences stimulation as a result of the pressure of the penis within her. Both partners are free to kiss and caress. The position is a favourite with many women.

33. Now the man has spread his legs, and linked them on his partner's buttocks. Penetration is very good, and by moving his hips from side to side, the man can give his partner considerable pleasure. The woman is able to make more definite movements, and the position is ideal for kissing.

34. Here the woman kneels astride the man. The penis is held firmly, and the woman can execute shallow up and down movements with safety. The position is a popular one, and affords great pleasure to both partners.

35. By lifting the man's bent knees, and raising them towards her back, the woman secures the penis even more firmly, and increases penetration. The man is free to caress her breasts, but all other movements must be made by the woman. The position is a strenuous one, and should not be maintained for long.

36. By leaning forward, the woman decreases penetration, but the position admits considerable small movements which are generally found to be most stimulating. Both partners can control the coital movements, but the initiative should remain with the woman who must avoid any precipitate movements, or the penis will slip out.

37. In this squatting position, provided she keeps her thighs as closely together as possible, the woman lessens the danger of the penis escaping. She is able to make good, deep movements, and penetration is excellent.

38. Another variant in which the woman, mainly, controls the coital movements, although the man can also make a valid, if less positive contribution. Both partners will find all movements most stimulating.

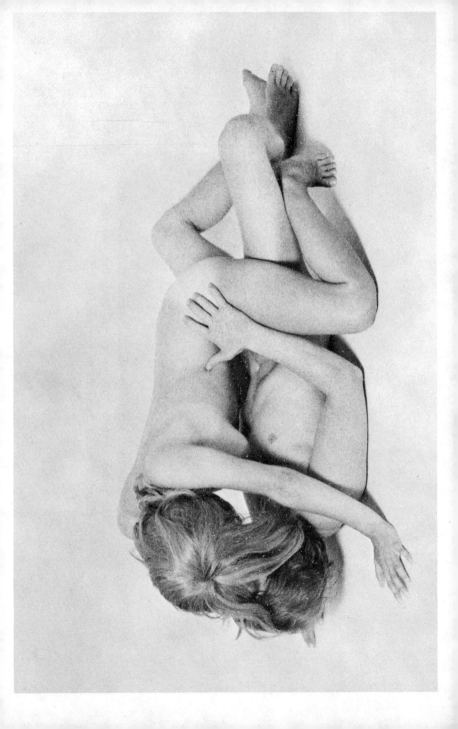

39. The man sits up, with the woman crouching over his penis. Penetration is deep, and the woman is afforded much freedom of movement.

40. By changing her position to a kneeling one, the woman permits greater penetration, but her movements are limited to shallow ones. This is, however, a favoured, and satisfactory position.

41. The man now supports the squatting woman on his thighs. The woman is able to make good up and down movements, and the man is able to prompt and guide her with his hands.

42. Even better movements are possible if the woman kneels, her weight still supported by the man's thighs. In this position, the woman's movements are very easy to make, and there is little danger of the penis escaping.

43. Here both partners kneel, the woman's legs being placed outside the man's. Penetration is reasonably good, and both partners are able to make good coital movements, as well as being free to kiss and caress.

44. Both partners extend their legs beyond the other's body. The woman is able to make small but effective movements, and penetration is good. The position is a tiring one for the woman, who places a considerable strain on her arms.

45. The man now lies down, while the woman remains in virtually the same position. This is an extremely good position for those who enjoy observing their lovemaking, but little movement is possible for either partner.

46. By placing one leg over her partner's shoulder, the woman experiences greater stimulation. Movement is limited, however, but since even slight movements are likely to be pleasurable this is not a serious disadvantage. The penis is not very securely held, and movements should be carefully controlled.

47. The woman now faces away from the man, and supports her weight on his thighs. She is kneeling, and is able to make good up and down movements. The man is also able to contribute to the movements. Penetration is quite good, and the position affords excellent stimulation.

48. The woman assumes the sitting position which although it maintains good penetration, severely limits movement. It is a good resting position, developing naturally from the former, without breaking the union.

49. By kneeling over the man, and grasping his knees, the woman can perform good up and down movements, or she can leave all the activity to the man, who is able to move his hips freely.

50. This position is particularly good for the woman, since most stimulation is against the back wall of the vagina. The man brings his knees up, and the woman leans against them. One leg can be dropped over the edge of the bed, or the woman can squat, or kneel. She is able to move freely, and even slight movements will produce good stimulation.

51. By squatting over the man, the woman limits her movements, but still experiences considerable stimulation. This is another effective and useful resting position, which still provides a reasonable degree of pleasure.

52. Although a very tiring position, this is a most pleasurable one. It is easier, if the man rests his back against a wall. The woman literally sits on the penis, and the man raises one or both of her legs. By keeping her legs closely together, the woman exerts considerable pressure on the penis, and penetration is extremely deep. By clenching and unclenching her buttocks, the woman can stimulate the penis, but no other movements are practical.

53. With her weight supported against the man's knees, the woman obtains good freedom of movement in the crouching position. Although pleasurable for both partners, it is a tiring position for the woman.

54. The woman faces the man's feet, and kneels astride him. There is a great danger of losing the penis in this position, which is perhaps best regarded as one of rest. It is, however, very stimulating for the woman.

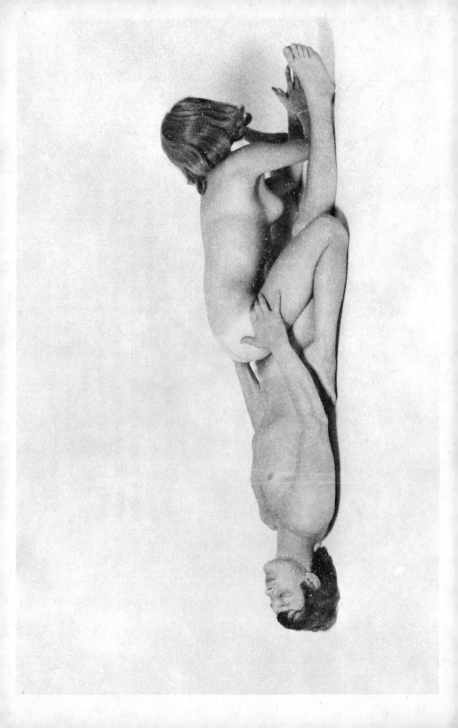

55. A variation of the previous position. The man raises his torso a little in order to grasp the woman's arms. Penetration is deep, and the back wall of the vagina is again greatly stimulated. A rocking movement backwards and forwards, executed simultaneously by both partners, is the most effective, and results in very pleasurable stimulation of the woman. It is, however, a difficult position to maintain for long, and both partners soon tire.

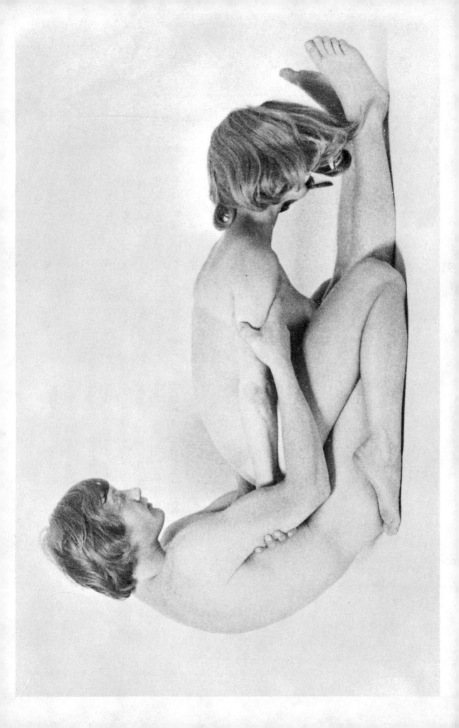

56. Literally a head to toe position which, although being very stimulating, curtails all movement but a slight circular motion of the woman's hips. This is, however, often extremely enjoyable for the woman, who experiences considerable pleasure from the pressure of the penis, and the slightest movements.

57. The man now kneels, with his buttocks resting on his heels. His weight is supported by his hands. The woman sits upon him, her feet braced. Penetration is reasonable, but movements are limited because of the danger of losing the penis. This is, however, a good resting position, and a starting point for a number of variations.

58. By assuming a squatting position, with splayed legs, the woman gives herself greater freedom of movement, and slightly increases penetration.

59. By kneeling before the man, with his knees between her spread thighs, the danger of losing the penis is greatly lessened. The man can make good, thrusting motions, while the woman is best advised to limit her activity to a side-to-side rocking movement. This causes good stimulation, which the man can augment by a limited thrusting.

60. The possibility of movement is greatly increased for both partners by the woman leaning even further forward, and supporting herself on her forearms. Considerable pressure is exerted within the vagina, which greatly stimulates the woman, despite the shallowness of penetration.

61. Using the end of a low bed, or a stool, the woman assumes a comfortable but essentially passive position. The woman's body should be fully extended, and her legs as widely parted as possible. The man has excellent access to the vagina, penetration is deep, and he has complete freedom to make and control the coital movements.

62. By supporting himself on his hands, his toes braced against the floor, the man enters his partner at an angle. The result is extremely stimulating, particularly for the woman, and the man is able to make long, deep thrusts that are mutually exciting.

63. The woman perches on the edge of the bed, or stool, the man kneeling between her legs. The man can thrust with a minimum of effort, and the woman is greatly stimulated.

64. By leaning backwards, taking her weight on her hands, the woman allows the man to straighten, and thus increases his freedom of movement. This is a very comfortable, untaxing position for the man, as well as being stimulating to both partners.

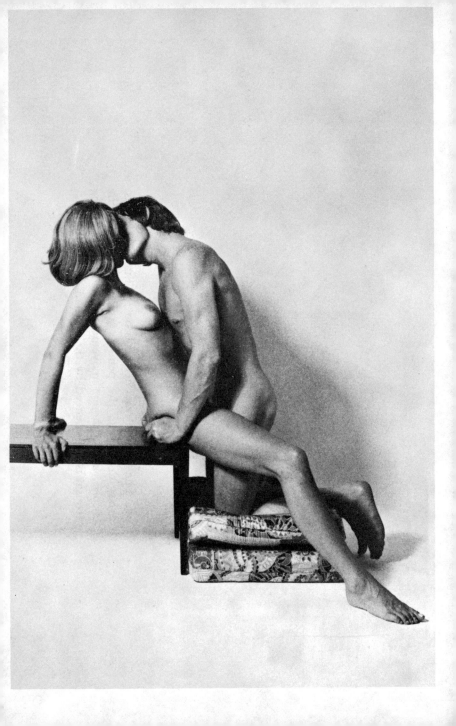

65. The woman rests her heels on the man's buttocks. From this angle, the penis is able to stimulate the clitoris, and although movements are limited, strong arousal is experienced by the woman.

66. A direct variation of the preceding position, which enables the woman to match counter movements to the man's, and to press her lower body firmly against his. This allows the woman a measure of control over movements which are extremely stimulating to her.

67. By linking her legs around the man, her heels against his buttocks, the woman enables greater depth of penetration. Again this is a very stimulating position for the woman, and allows the man complete freedom of movement, with maximum penetration. It is taxing on neither partner, and gives the man complete control.

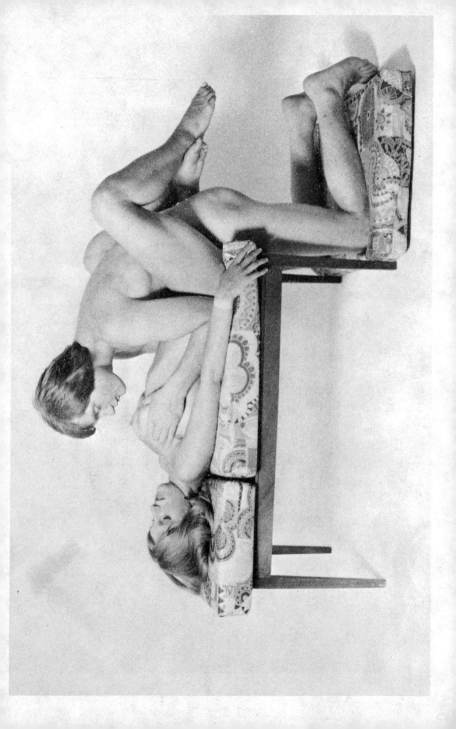

68. By raising her legs even higher, the woman is able to partially support the man. Again penetration is excellent, there is a lot of freedom of movement, and great stimulation for the woman.

69. The woman's legs hook over the man's shoulders. By keeping her thighs as closely together as possible, pressure is brought to bear on the penis. In this position, the woman can also make some movements of her own. Penetration remains deep, and the man's freedom to move is unimpaired.

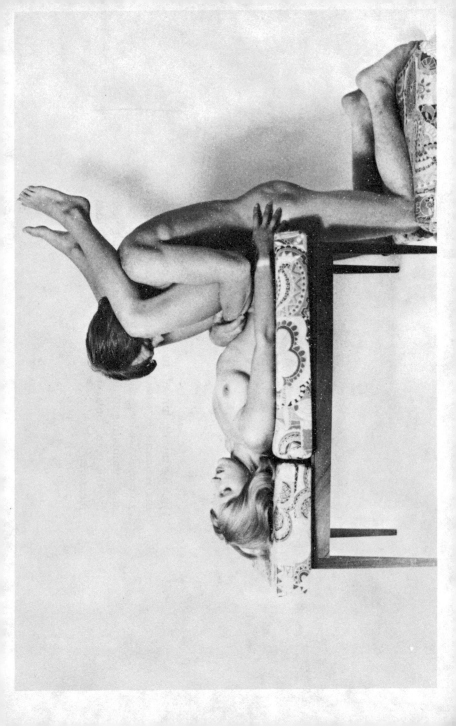

70. By raising himself to a diagonal position, forcing the woman's legs back against her breasts, the man is able to make long, deep movements which are remarkably stimulating to the woman. This is a tiring position for the man, but one which affords a great deal of pleasure.

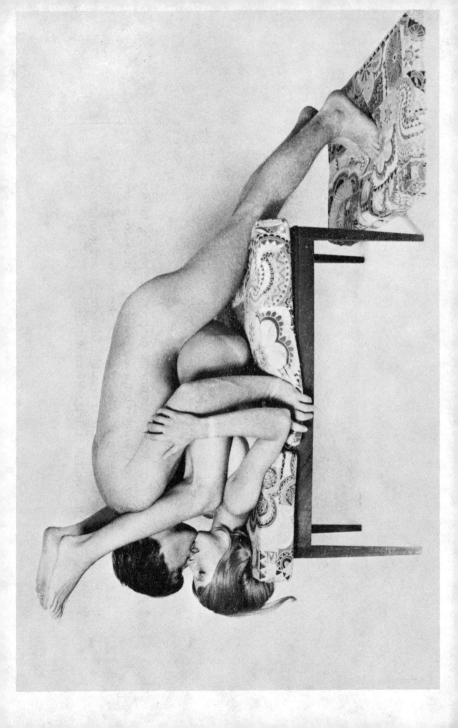

71. The woman assumes a deep crouch which, unlike other rear entry positions, enables the man to penetrate deeply. It is necessary for the woman to spread her thighs as far as possible. Movements are good, and the position is mutually stimulating.

72. The woman turns on to her side, and her calves are supported by the stool. The man gains great freedom of movement, and the angle of entry is very stimulating to the woman.

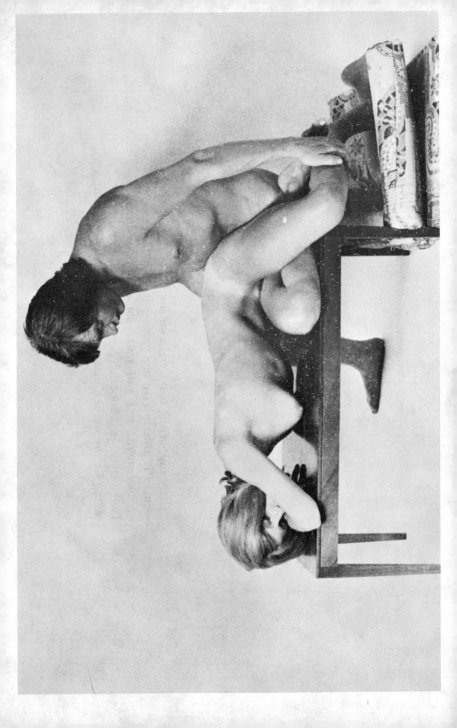

73. By supporting her weight on the bed, or stool, the woman is able to give her partner maximum freedom of movement, and can make some motions herself. Penetration is reasonable, and the position is less taxing for the woman than when it is executed without support.

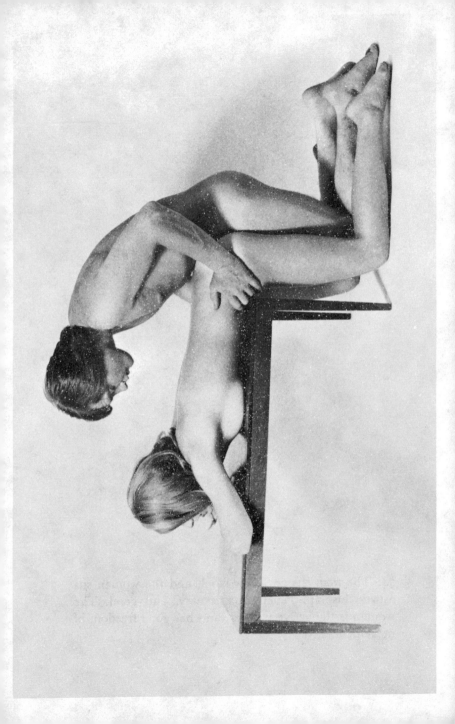

74. The man sits on a low stool, and the woman sits astride his lap. Penetration is easy, and good. The woman is the active partner, and has good freedom of movement.

75. The man lies on his back, his feet reaching to the floor. The woman astride him also supports herself by her feet on the floor. This is a very comfortable, relaxed position for both man and woman. Penetration is deep, and there is little danger of losing the penis, although the woman can make quite free movements.

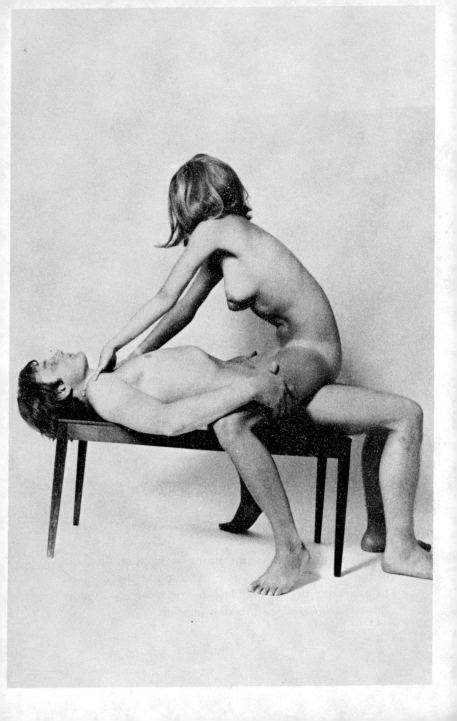

76. By raising his legs, and resting his heels on the foot of the bed, or stool, the man can support the woman to a greater degree, and aid her movements. Again this is a comfortable, untaxing position.

77. The woman sits with her back to the man, as in position 74. Again she has good freedom of movement, particularly if she leans down and supports her weight with her hands. She can then raise her haunches easily, and in a controlled manner.

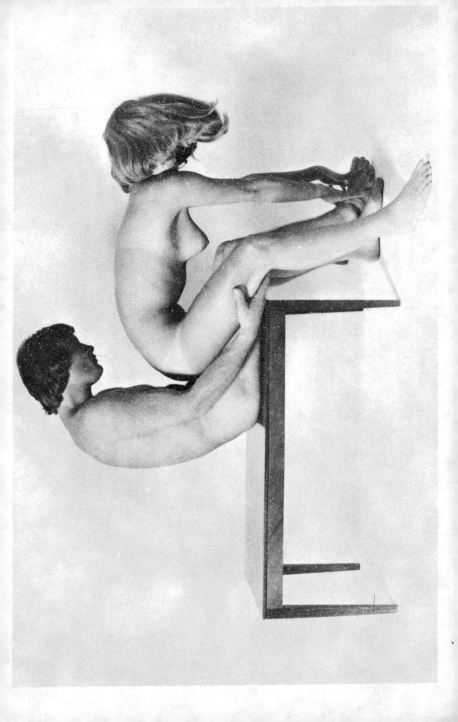

78. With the man lying down, his legs on the floor, the woman straddles him, facing his feet. Her movements must be small, to avoid loss of the penis, but stimulation is good, and is obtained from quite slight motions.

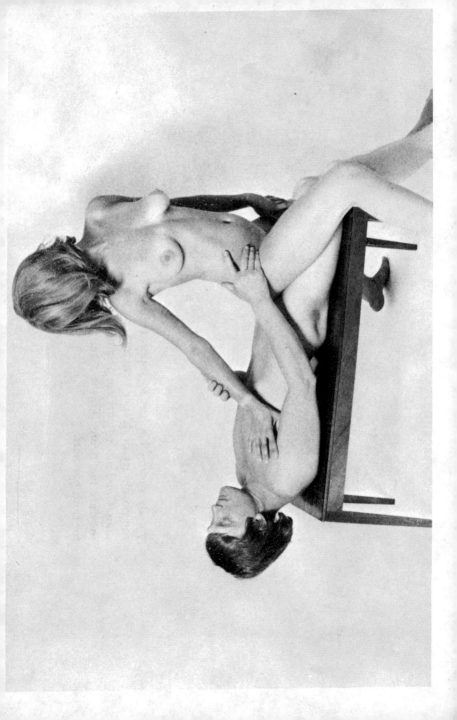

79. By raising his legs to support the woman's torso, the possibility of deeper penetration is created by the man. Good movements are possible by the woman, and they are less tiring. This is a very stimulating position for both partners.

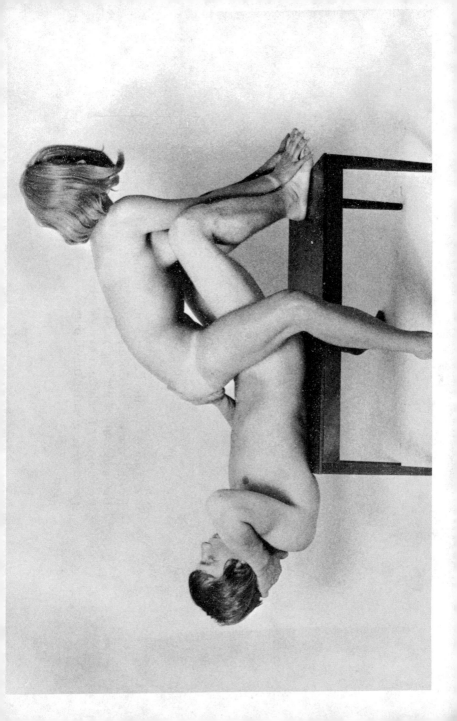

80. Another position that is outstandingly rewarding for the woman, producing much stimulation against the back wall of her vagina. Moreover, she is able to move fairly freely and even slight movements will prove to be greatly stimulating.

81. There are some interesting positions which require the use of a chair. Opposite we show the basic pose, the starting point for variations which are demonstrated in the following pages.

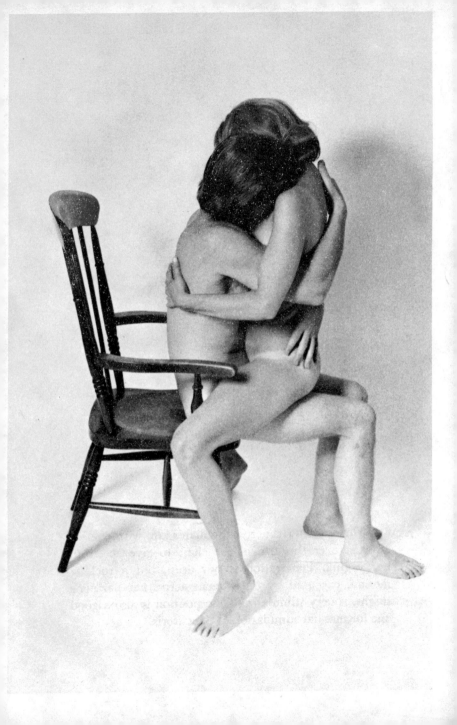

82. The woman sits across the man's lap, with one leg crooked over the arm of the chair to give access to her vagina. Penetration is not deep, but a rocking motion, executed by the woman across her partner's thighs, is very stimulating. The position is also a good one for manual stimulation of the clitoris.

83. The woman sits on the man's lap, but faces away from him. She can, again, make rocking motions, while the man is able to contribute side-to-side movements of his hips. The front wall of the vagina is greatly stimulated, and the position is a comfortable one, particularly if the woman takes her weight on her hands, which rest on the man's knees.

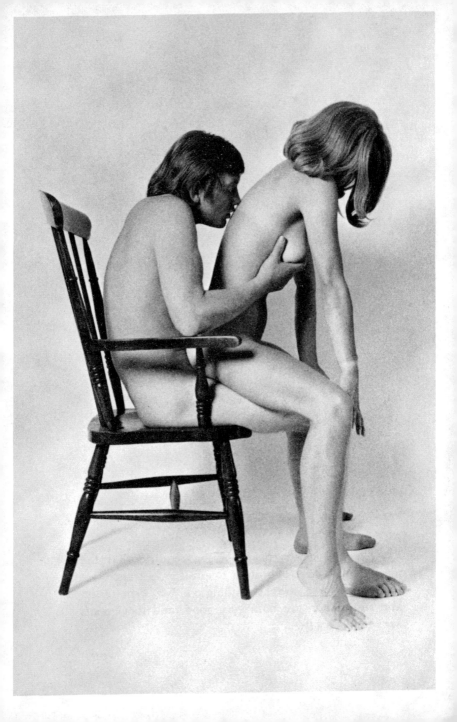

84. The classical vertical position requires that the man bend his knees in order to effect an entrance. He then returns to a normal standing position. Penetration and stimulation are both very good, and movements are reasonably free.

85. This is an extremely difficult position, requiring a good sense of balance on the part of both partners. Each person stands on one leg, after penetration, and the other leg is hooked around the partner's hip. Movements are necessarily slight, but a great deal of pressure is exerted both on the penis, and within the vagina. The position, of course, cannot be maintained for more than a few moments, but stimulation is good, and the position presents an interesting, if extreme, variation.

86. This position is particularly good for partners whose height differs considerably. The man lifts the woman until penetration is possible, and then draws her on to his penis. The woman links her legs around his buttocks, clasping her arms around his neck. This is a very stimulating position, with both partners being free to move. It is, however, obviously tiring in the extreme, and cannot be maintained for long.

87. Entrance is effected from the rear, and in most cases, the woman will have to bend forward to facilitate entry. Penetration is very shallow, and the movements are severely restricted. The position does allow manual stimulation of the clitoris, however, and the woman's body can easily be caressed.

88. By bending forward, the woman allows greater penetration, although this is still not deep. The man can move a little more freely, however, and his hands remain free to caress.

90. Although every muscle is in a position of rest, the woman is in an exciting posture. The woman supports the weight of her hands, and is supported in the hips by the hands of the man, so that mutual relaxation of the muscles provides the greatest enjoyment.

89. Although very strenuous, particularly for the woman, this is an exciting position. The woman supports her weight on her hands, and is supported at the hips by the man. Penetration is deep, and very stimulating. The man is able to make brusque, forceful, controlled movements.

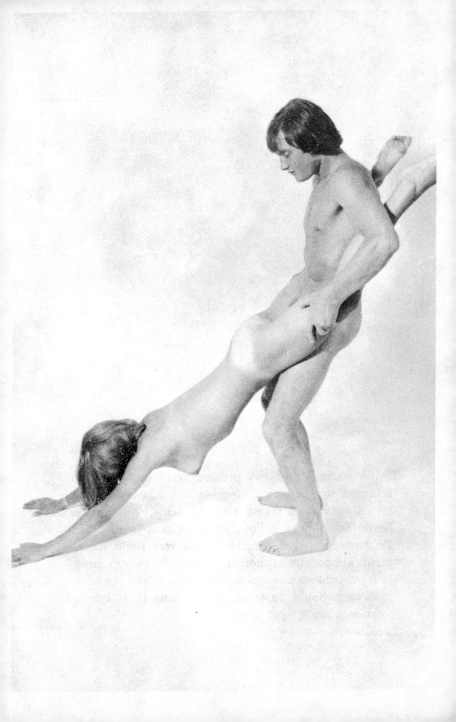

90. A variation of the previous position, which is achieved by the woman locking her legs behind the man's back, and taking some of her weight on her head. For this, a pillow, or a cushion is essential. Penetration is very deep, but only very slight movements are possible, although these can be very exciting. It is an arduous position for the woman, and considerable care should be taken in executing it. It can be held only for a short time.